▶▶ KEY POINTS

▶ Place value means that each digit in a number h[...]
  its position in the number.
▶ Each digit is worth 10 times more than the digit to its right and
  10 times less that the digit on its left.
▶ The decimal point separates whole numbers from decimal fractions,
  eg, tenths, hundredths, thousandths.

1 Write these numbers in figures.

(a) Eight thousand and five

(b) Thirteen thousand, one hundred and fifty-seven

(c) Seven point five two   *[3 marks]*

2 For each set of numbers, put a ring around the smallest number
and underline the largest number.

(a)   3.12   2.123   3.123   3.012   3.001   2.312

(b)   12.95   11.06   12.45   11.98   12.021   11.3   *[2 marks]*

3 Write down the value of the number 3 in each of these numbers.

(a) 17 263 ....

(b) 1340   ....

(c) 59.3   ....   *[3 marks]*

4 Here are four digit cards. | 0 | 9 | 5 | 1 |

(a) What is the smallest number
    you can make using all four cards?

(b) What is the largest number
    you can make using all four cards?   *[2 marks]*

1

▶▶ KEY POINTS

▶ Numbers may be ordered by comparing the place value of their digits.
▶ The signs <, >, ≤, ≥ and = can be used to compare numbers. The widest part of the > sign always points towards the larger number.

1 Put these car prices in order, starting with the smallest.

£13 416   £14 316   £31 614   £11 346   £13 146

....   *[1 mark]*

2 Put these masses in order, starting with the heaviest.

5.05 kg   55.0 kg   5.0 kg   0.55 kg   5.5 kg

....   *[1 mark]*

3 Find and mark the position of the following numbers on the number line:

3.8   3.95   4.2   3.75

3.7   4.0   4.3   *[2 marks]*

4 Put the < sign or the > sign in the box to make each of these number sentences correct.

(a) 135 cm ☐ 153 cm   (b) 1076 ml ☐ 1067 ml

(c) 0.03 ☐ 0.3   *[3 marks]*

5 Write down a number which comes between:

(a) 63 and 78   ....

(b) 5.6 and 5.7   ....

(c) 9 998 and 10 005   ....   *[3 marks]*

▶▶ KEY POINTS

▶ Look at the digit after the digit to which the number is to be rounded. If it is 4 or less, the number may be rounded down; if it is 5 or more, it is rounded up.

▶ Decimal numbers may be rounded to have one decimal place; this means one digit to the right of the decimal point (in the tenths column).

1 Kerry's local football team is Barnstone Rovers.
The numbers of people attending the team's last three games are listed in the table below.
Round each of these numbers (a) to the nearest hundred and (b) to the nearest ten.

Date	Attendance	Nearest 100	Nearest 10
Saturday 4th October	1678		
Saturday 11th October	832		
Saturday 18th October	1054		

[3 marks]

2 Circle the number below that is nearest in value to 630.

599   699   701   656   530   600

[1 mark]

3 (a) Round all the decimals below to one decimal place.

0.45   0.62   0.51   0.89   0.09

....

(b) Circle any decimals above which will round to 1 as their nearest whole number.

[2 marks]

4 Which of these calculations will work out to approximately 200?
Put a tick next to those that you think will.

136 + 80 ☐   19 x 9 ☐   20 x 40 ☐   315 – 158 ☐   *[2 marks]*

> **▶▶ KEY POINTS**

▶ There are four types of triangle: **right-angled** (one angle of 90°), **equilateral** (all sides and angles are equal), **isosceles** (two equal sides and angles) and **scalene** (no equal sides or angles).
▶ Polygons have straight sides. Regular polygons have sides of equal length; irregular polygons have sides of different lengths.
▶ A **pentagon** has 5 sides, a **hexagon** has 6 sides, a **heptagon** has 7 sides, an **octagon** has 8 sides.

I Look at the triangles below.
Put an **E** inside the equilateral triangle,
an **I** inside the isosceles triangle,
and an **R** inside the right-angled triangle.

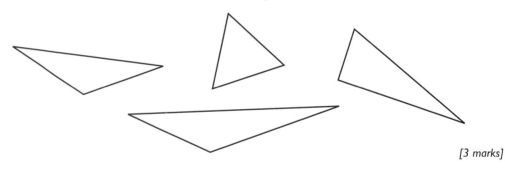

[3 marks]

2 Put a tick next to the statements which are **true**.
Put a cross next to the statements which are **false**.

An isosceles triangle has 3 equal sides. ☐

A scalene triangle has no equal sides. ☐

An isosceles triangle has 2 equal angles. ☐

An equilateral triangle has one pair of parallel sides. ☐

The angles inside an equilateral triangle add up to 360°. ☐

[5 marks]

3 Brian has made a chart to classify shapes.
He has not finished filling it in.
Look at the shapes and their properties and help Brian to complete
his chart.

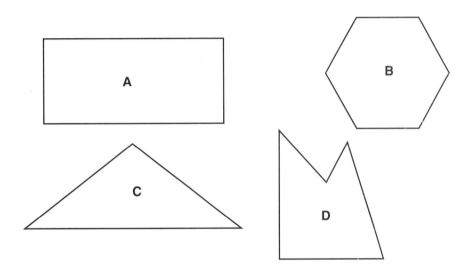

Put a tick if the statement is **true** or a cross if it is **false**.

Shape	Parallel sides	All sides of equal length	Has at least one right angle
A		✗	✓
B	✓		✗
C			✗
D	✗		

[3 marks]   **5**

▶▶ **KEY POINTS**

▶ Quadrilaterals are four-sided shapes. Quadrilateral means four-sided.
▶ Some quadrilaterals have special names, such as: square, rectangle, rhombus, parallelogram, trapezium and kite.
▶ Quadrilaterals can be classified according to their properties: equal sides, number of right angles, pairs of parallel lines.

1. Look at the quadrilaterals below.
   Name each quadrilateral and mark any pairs of parallel lines.

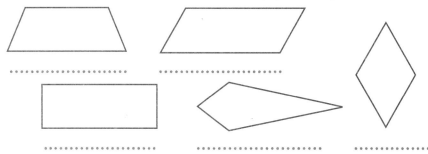

....

[5 marks]

....

2. Draw a quadrilateral
   with four right angles
   and two pairs of parallel lines.

[1 mark]

3. Draw a quadrilateral
   with no right angles.

[1 mark]

4. Put a tick inside the shapes that are quadrilaterals.

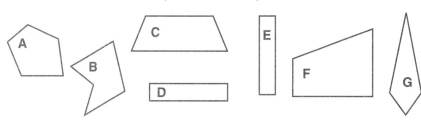

[1 mark]

> ## ▶▶ KEY POINTS

> ▶ Addition is the inverse of subtraction.
> ▶ Look for doubles or near doubles, or numbers which add up to 1, 10 or 100 and add them first.
> ▶ Read problems carefully. Look for the words to do with addition, eg, total, sum, altogether.
> ▶ Always check your addition using a different method, or a calculator.

1 Calculate:

(a) 16 + 17 + 18 ....

(b) 345 + 279 ....

(c) 5.5 + 0.9 ....   *[3 marks]*

2 Write the missing numbers in each number sentence.

(a) 92 + ☐ = 113

(b) ☐6☐ + ☐4☐ = 100

(c) 200 – ☐ = 58   *[3 marks]*

3 Circle a pair of numbers below which gives a total of 100.

　　43　　　　86　　　　39　　　　57　　　　15　　　　61

[1 mark]

4 Write in the missing numbers so that each side of the triangle has a total of 1.

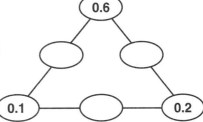

[1 mark]

▶▶ (KEY) POINTS

▶ Subtraction is the inverse of addition.
▶ In a subtraction problem, the answer will be less than the largest number you started with.
▶ Answers to subtraction problems may be checked by using addition.

1 Write in the missing numbers to make these calculations correct.

(a) 200 − [   ] = 134

(b) [8 | 7 |] − [| 5 | 4] = 617   *[2 marks]*

2 Circle the pair of numbers with the greater difference.

123 − 45   129 − 56

[1 mark]

3 Liam and Polly each have some pocket money to spend.
Liam has £5 and spends £3.67. How much does he have left?

£ [   ]

Polly has £12 and buys a CD costing £2.99.
How much change does she receive?

£ [   ]   *[2 marks]*

4 Calculate **1807 − 769**

[   ]   *[1 mark]*

5 179 passengers board an empty train.
38 passengers get off the train at the first station.
54 passengers get off the train at the second station.
How many passengers are left on the train after the second stop?

[   ]   *[1 mark]*

▶▶ KEY POINTS

▶ A line of symmetry, when it is drawn through a 2D shape, divides the shape so that it is exactly the same on both sides of the line; this is also called reflective symmetry.
▶ A shape may have more than one line of symmetry.
▶ Lines of symmetry may not only be horizontal or vertical.
▶ A regular polygon (many-sided shape) has as many lines of symmetry as it has sides. For example, a regular pentagon has 5 lines of symmetry.

1 Draw in all the lines of symmetry you can see in these shapes.

A   B    C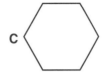

[3 marks]

2 Complete the pattern below, which is symmetrical about the straight black line.

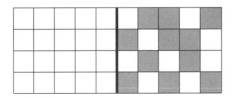

[1 mark]

3 Tick inside the shapes below that have reflective symmetry.

A    B    C    D

[1 mark]

4 Complete the shape on the right, which has reflective symmetry about the straight black line.

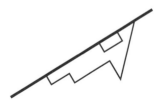

[1 mark]   9

▶▶ KEY POINTS

▶ 3D shapes have height, width and depth; they are solid shapes.
▶ 3D shapes have edges, faces and vertices.
▶ A vertex is a point at which edges meet; it is another word for corner.
▶ Some shapes, such as cones, spheres and cylinders, have curved faces.
▶ Prisms have the same shaped face at both ends.
▶ If you were to unfold a 3D shape and draw round the outline,
   you would have its net.

1 Claire and Sean have been looking at 3D shapes.
They have been counting the edges, faces and vertices.

Complete the table.

Shape		Faces	Edges	Vertices
Cylinder		3		
Cuboid			12	
Triangular prism		5		6
Square-based pyramid			8	
Cone			1	

[5 marks]

2 Here are some nets.
Some of them will fold up to make up a square-based pyramid and some will not.
Tick the nets that will form a complete shape and put a cross inside those that will not.

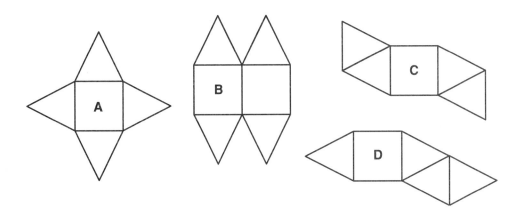

[2 marks]

3 Draw a net of the open box shown in the picture.

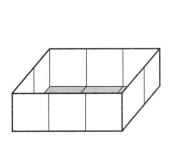
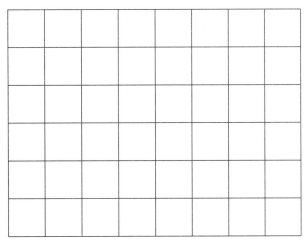

[1 mark]　　**11**

▶▶ KEY POINT

▶ Multiplication is the inverse of division, eg, if $3 \times 9 = 27$ then $27 \div 9 = 3$.

1 Write what the missing numbers could be.

$4 \times 12 = $ ☐   ☐ $\times 7 = 63$ ☐ $\times$ ☐ $= 54$

[3 marks]

2 What number when multiplied by 7 makes 35? ☐

[1 mark]

3 Look at this multiplication: 6×4
Find two more numbers which multiply together to give
the same product. Write your numbers in the boxes below.

 ☐ $\times$ ☐

[1 mark]

4 Complete the multiplication grid
opposite. One square in the grid
has been completed for you.

×	5	3
6	30	
5		

[1 mark]

5 A chef uses four boxes of eggs to make a large quantity of fresh
custard. Eggs are packed in boxes of six. How many eggs does
the chef use to make the custard?

☐

[1 mark]

6 A football club has booked 7 coaches to take supporters to a cup
match. Each coach can seat 52 passengers. How many supporters can
travel on the coaches provided?

☐

[1 mark]

7 Shaun knows that $36 \times 18 = 648$
Explain how he can write down the answer to 18×18 without working
out the multiplication.

[1 mark]

▶▶ (KEY) POINTS

▶ Even numbers end in 0, 2, 4, 6, 8; odd numbers end in 1, 3, 5, 7, 9.
▶ Multiples are the answers to multiplication tables.
▶ Factors are numbers that divide exactly into a number.
▶ A prime number has only two factors: 1 and the number itself.
▶ A square number is found by multiplying a number by itself,
   eg, 4 squared, or $4^2 = 4 \times 4 = 16$.

1 Complete this three-digit number
   so that it is a multiple of 7.

3		

[1 mark]

2 Circle the numbers that are prime numbers.

   9   7   13   16   27

[1 mark]

3 Write down a two-digit even number
   that is also a square number.

[1 mark]

4 Write down a number that has
   the factors 5 and 6.

[1 mark]

5 A bakery makes 12 852 jam tarts in one day.
   The tarts are packed into boxes of three.
   (a) Without dividing the number of tarts by 3, explain how it is
       possible to say that there will be no tarts left over after packing.

   ....

   (b) The bakery decides to pack the tarts into boxes of four.
       Explain how you can check whether there will be any tarts
       left over after packing.

   .... [2 marks]

6 Harpreet and Joe count aloud together from 1 to 30.
   Harpreet bangs a drum on every third number.
   Joe rings a bell on every fifth number.
   How many times will the drum and bell sound together?

[1 mark]

13

▶▶ KEY POINTS

▶ A sequence is a list of numbers which are linked by a rule.
▶ The sequence of square numbers starts 1, 4, 9, 16, 25, 36, 49, 64...

1 Fill in the missing numbers in the sequence. Explain the rule for the sequence.

37, 29, ☐ , 13, ☐   ....

[1 mark]

2 Jenna makes pendants of different sizes. She uses rubies (●) and diamonds (◊) to make the designs.

Size 1   Size 2   Size 3

(a) How many rubies will Jenna need to make a size 6 pendant?   ☐

(b) How many rubies will a pendant with 16 diamonds have?   ☐

[2 marks]

3 The first five multiples of 35 are listed as a sequence below.

35   70   105   140   175

Henry says, "If the sequence is continued, the twelfth number will be 425." Without working out the twelfth number, explain why Henry is wrong.

[1 mark]

....

4 Jodie is making number sequences. In one sequence, she starts with the number 3 and makes the next number in the sequence by adding 11. Write down the next three numbers in her sequence.

3   ☐

[1 mark]

▶▶ KEY POINTS

▶ One whole turn is 360°; one quarter turn is 90°, or a right angle.

▶ Two right angles (180°) make a straight line; four right angles (360°) make a whole turn.

▶ An angle less than 90° is acute; an angle between 90° and 180° is obtuse; an angle greater than 180° is reflex.

▶ Angles in a straight line add up to 180°, angles at a point add up to 360°, angles inside a triangle add up to 180° and each angle in an equilateral triangle measures 60°.

1 Complete the table.

number of right angles	$\frac{1}{2}$	1	$1\frac{1}{2}$			4
degrees		90°		180°	270°	

[2 marks]

2 Look at the angle opposite.

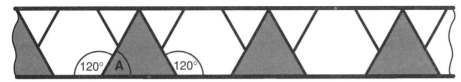

For each sentence, put a tick if it is true or a cross if it is false.

The angle is an obtuse angle. ☐   The angle is greater than 45° ☐

The angle is less than a right angle. ☐   The angle is an acute angle. ☐

[2 marks]

3 Here is a piece of wallpaper border.

Work out the size of angle A.
Do not use a protractor to measure it.

☐ °

[1 mark]

What type of triangle is each grey triangle?
Put a tick in the correct box.

isosceles ☐   right-angled ☐   equilateral ☐   scalene ☐

[1 mark]

4 Asim cut out a triangle from a piece of paper.
He measured two of the angles with a protractor.
He did not measure the third angle but said
that it must be **38°**.
Explain why Asim is correct.

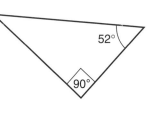

[1 mark]

5 A slice of pizza is cut from a whole pizza.

(a) Measure angle **A**.

(b) Calculate angle **B**.

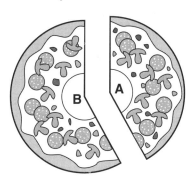

[2 marks]

6 Measure angle **A**. Write your answer in the box.

[1 mark]

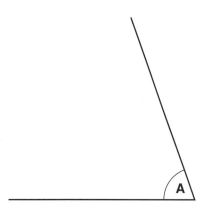

Use a protractor and a ruler to draw an angle which is larger than **A**
but smaller than 80°. Draw your angle in the box above.

[1 mark]

▶▶ **KEY** POINTS

▶ Probability is a measure of how likely it is for something to happen.
▶ Some events have equally likely outcomes, eg, tossing a coin, rolling a dice.
▶ All probabilities lie between 0 (impossible) and 1 (certain).

1 The four spinners below can land on either black or white.
Put a tick next to the spinner which is most likely to land on white.

 ☐ ☐ 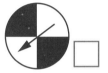 ☐ ☐   *[1 mark]*

2 The spinner below can land on the numbers 1, 2, or 3.

(a) What is the probability of the spinner landing on 3? ☐

(b) Which number is the spinner most likely to land on? ☐

Give a reason. .... *[3 marks]*

3 Sita has placed some shapes in a box.
Without looking, she takes one shape out of the box.

Only one of the following statements is true.
Put a tick in the box next to the true statement.

It is unlikely that Sita will take out a star. ☐
It is equally likely that Sita will take out a star. ☐
It is certain that Sita will take out a star. ☐   *[1 mark]*

4 A bag contains 10 green balls.
How many white balls must be added to the bag so that there is an even chance of taking a green ball out at random?

[1 mark]   **17**

▶▶ KEY POINT

▶ Division is the inverse of multiplication, eg, if $40 \div 5 = 8$ then $8 \times 5 = 40$.

1 Circle the division questions which have the answer 6.

$14 \div 2$ $24 \div 4$ $27 \div 3$ $32 \div 4$ $30 \div 5$

[1 mark]

2 Write the missing number.

$44 \div \boxed{} = 11$

[1 mark]

3 Jake writes a number on a card.
He asks Frances to guess the number on the card by giving her a clue.
He says, "If I divide the number on the card by 4 it gives the answer 32."
What is the number on the card?

[1 mark]

4 Calculate:

(a) $127 \div 7 = \boxed{}$ (b) $365 \div 24 = \boxed{}$ *[2 marks]*

5 Look at this multiplication fact. $6 \times 27 = 162$

Use this to write down the answer to $162 \div 27 = \boxed{}$ *[1 mark]*

6 Tony has made 58 toffee cakes for the cake stall at the school fair.
He decides to put four cakes in a bag. How many bags can he fill?

[1 mark]

7 Kylie's teacher has asked her to work out the answer to $108 \div 18$.
Explain how Kylie can use the two division statements below to
work out the answer to the teacher's question.

$108 \div 2 = 54$ $54 \div 9 = 6$

[1 mark]

▶▶ KEY POINTS

▶ To **multiply** a number by 10/100/1000 move the digits 1/2/3 places to the left.

▶ To **divide** a number by 10/100/1000 move the digits 1/2/3 places to the right.

1 Write in the missing numbers.

(a) 67 × 10 = ☐

(b) 9000 ÷ 100 = ☐

(c) 832 × ☐ = 83 200

(d) 260 ÷ ☐ = 26

(e) 5.7 × 10 = ☐

(f) ☐ ÷ 10 = 0.8

(g) 40 × 70 = ☐

(h) 50 × 7 = ☐

(i) 140 ÷ 20 = ☐

(j) ☐ × 50 = 2500   *[10 marks]*

2 What number is 10 times smaller than 32?   ☐ *[1 mark]*

3 How many times larger is 5600 than 56?   ☐ *[1 mark]*

4 Each day Donna delivers 53 newspapers on her paper round. How many newspapers will she have delivered in 100 days?

☐ *[1 mark]*

5 Kerry's uncle has 150 lettuce seeds which he wants to sow in his vegetable garden.
He has prepared 10 rows in which to plant the seeds.
How many seeds should he sow in each row?

☐ *[1 mark]*

6 Heechan has asked each child in his school to bring in 20 milk bottle tops for a charity appeal.
There are 90 children in Heechan's school.
How many milk bottle tops can he expect to collect?   *[1 mark]*

19

▶▶ **KEY** POINTS

▶ **Length** I kilometre (km) = 1000 metres (m); I metre = 100 centimetres (cm); I centimetre = 10 millimetres.

▶ **Mass** I tonne (t) = 1000 kilograms (kg); I kilogram = 1000 grams (g).

▶ **Capacity** I litre (l) = 1000 millilitres (ml); I litre = 100 centilitres (cl); I centilitre = 10 millilitres.

▶ **Length** 8 kilometres is about 5 miles.

▶ **Mass** I kilogram is about 2 pounds (lb); 30 grams is about I ounce (oz).

▶ **Capacity** I litre is about 2 pints; 4.5 litres is about I gallon, or 8 pints.

1 Complete the following statements.

(a) There are ☐ grams in I kilogram.

(b) There are ☐ centimetres in I metre.

(c) I centilitre is the same amount as ☐ millilitres.   *[3 marks]*

2 Cathy is using a recipe which gives quantities in imperial units. She knows the following relationships between units.

Imperial	Metric
2 pounds	I kilogram
I ounce	30 grams

(a) The recipe needs I pound of flour. How many **kilograms** of flour is this? ☐ kg

(b) The recipe needs 4 ounces of sugar. How many **grams** of sugar is this? ☐ g   *[2 marks]*

3 Gary measures the length of his pet hamster. His hamster is 9.6 cm long. How long is the hamster in mm? ☐ mm

Gary then weighs his hamster. His hamster is 0.15 kg. How much does his hamster weigh in grams? ☐ g   *[2 marks]*

▶▶ KEY POINT

▶ Work out how much each division (mark) on the scale is worth before taking a reading.

1 Join the objects to their correct masses. One has been done for you.

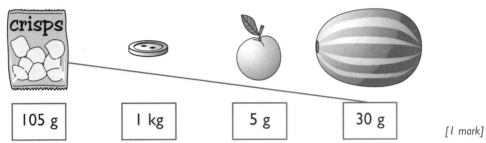

| 105 g | 1 kg | 5 g | 30 g |

[1 mark]

2 360 ml of milk is poured into a measuring jug.

Draw the level of milk in the jug.

[1 mark]

3 Shelley has weighed out some flour on a set of kitchen scales. The scales can be used to measure in grams or ounces.

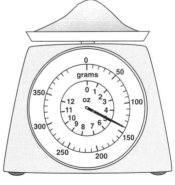

How many **grams (g)** does the flour weigh?   ☐ g

How many **ounces (oz)** does the flour weigh?   ☐ oz   *[2 marks]*

▶▶ KEY POINTS

▶ Equivalent fractions represent the same quantity.
▶ A mixed number is made up of a whole number and a fraction, eg, $5\frac{1}{2}$.
▶ An improper fraction has a numerator (top number) which is larger than the denominator (bottom number).
▶ Fractions can be compared by converting them so that they have the same denominator.

1 Part of the shape below is shaded.

Answer the following, giving your fractions in their simplest form:

What fraction of the shape is shaded?

What fraction of the shape is not shaded?   *[1 mark]*

2 Circle all the fractions equivalent to $\frac{1}{2}$:

$\dfrac{4}{6}$ $\dfrac{5}{10}$ $\dfrac{18}{36}$ $\dfrac{9}{16}$ $\dfrac{50}{100}$ $\dfrac{7}{12}$ *[1 mark]*

3 Complete these equivalent fractions:

$\dfrac{5}{8} = \dfrac{}{16}$ $\dfrac{3}{4} = \dfrac{6}{}$ $\dfrac{3}{10} = \dfrac{}{100}$

[3 marks]

4 Change these improper fractions into their equivalent mixed numbers:

(a) $\dfrac{9}{4}$ (b) $\dfrac{18}{5}$

[2 marks]

5 Put these fractions in order from smallest to largest:

$\dfrac{1}{2}$ $\dfrac{3}{4}$ $\dfrac{7}{8}$ $\dfrac{5}{8}$ $\dfrac{10}{12}$

[1 mark]

▶▶ KEY POINTS

▶ A division can be written as a fraction, eg, $3 \div 4 = \frac{3}{4}$; $13 \div 5 = \frac{13}{5}$.

▶ To find a fraction of an amount, divide the amount by the denominator and then multiply by the numerator. For example, to find $\frac{3}{4}$ of an amount, divide the amount by 4 and then multiply by 3.

1 How many halves are there in $3\frac{1}{2}$?   [1 mark]

2 Kelvin has 45 sweets.
He gives $\frac{1}{5}$ of them to Omar.
How many does he have left?   [1 mark]

3 (a) What is $\frac{3}{4}$ of £200?   £   [1 mark]

(b) Explain how you worked out your answer.   [1 mark]

....

4 How many minutes are there in $3\frac{1}{4}$ hours?   minutes   [1 mark]

5 What fraction of £1 is 60p?
Give your answer as a fraction in its simplest form.   [1 mark]

6 What fraction of a metre is 19 cm?   [1 mark]

7 In a pencil box, there are 30 pencils.
$\frac{2}{3}$ of them are blue $\frac{1}{10}$ of them are red
$\frac{1}{15}$ of them are yellow $\frac{1}{6}$ of them are green.

Work out how many pencils there are of each colour.

    blue   red

    yellow   green   [1 mark)

▶▶ **KEY** POINTS

▶ The mode of a set of data is the most commonly occurring item or number.

▶ The range of a set of data is the difference between the largest number and the smallest number.

▶ The median of a set of data, in order of size, is the middle value.

▶ The mean is found by adding up all the values and dividing the total by the number of values.

1 Louise recorded the shoe sizes of eleven people in her class.

2, 4, 4, 2, 5, 2, 3, 6, 2, 5, 3

Shoe Size	Tally	Frequency
2		
3		
4		
5		
6		

(a) Record the data in the tally chart.

(b) What is the mode of the shoe sizes? ☐

(c) What is the range of shoe sizes? ☐

(d) Write the shoe sizes in a list, starting with the smallest.

....

What is the median shoe size? ☐ *[4 marks]*

2 Here are some scores in a spelling test:

Jane	10	Billy	10
Michaela	5	Ben	8
Kevin	6	Rachel	7
Anne	10		

Work out the mean score. ☐ *[1 mark]*

▶▶ KEY POINT

▶ Data may be displayed in pictograms, bar charts, bar line charts, line graphs, pie charts, tally charts and grouped frequency tables, Venn and Carroll diagrams.

1 Sally is sorting whole numbers. She decides to use a Venn diagram. Write the numbers in the correct sections of the diagram.

12   3   9   18   2   27   4   45

factors of 36 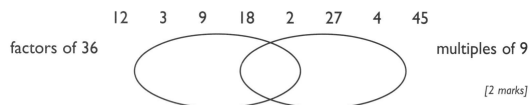 multiples of 9

[2 marks]

2 This Carroll diagram shows how some numbers between 15 and 25 have been sorted.

	Odd	not odd
Less than 20	19	14
Not less than 20		22

Add the numbers **18** and **23** to the diagram.

[1 mark]

3 Here is a line graph showing Samir's bicycle ride.
Answer the following questions using the information in the graph:

(a) What time did Samir start his journey?

(b) How far did Samir travel between 11 a.m. and 11.30 a.m.?

km

(c) What did Samir do between 12 noon and 12.30 p.m.?

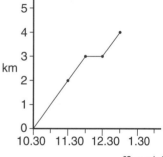

[3 marks]

4 Andrew's school has been raising money for a new minibus.
The school needs to raise £10 000.
Here is a bar chart showing the money raised.

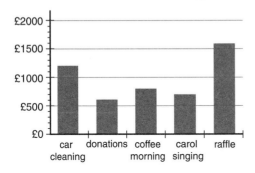

(a) Which activity made the most money? ....

(b) How much have they raised altogether? £ ☐

(c) How much short of their target are they? £ ☐

(d) Which activities raised more than £800?

[4 marks]

5 This pie chart shows the amount of time spent each week on different subjects at Westcott Primary School. Use the chart to help you answer the following questions:

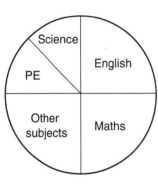

24 hours

(a) How many hours are spent on English? ☐ hours

(b) How many hours are spent on Science? ☐ hours

[2 marks]

▶▶ KEY POINTS

▶ Some answers on a calculator display will look different from what you see when you work them out with pencil and paper. For example, £1.50 would look like 1.5. You must learn to read them carefully.

▶ Sometimes you may need to round an answer up or down to the nearest whole number or to one decimal place.

▶ Check answers worked out on a calculator by using an inverse calculation, or by estimating an approximate answer before you start.

1 Rebecca is 150 cm tall and Natalie is 173 cm tall.
Stefanie's height is exactly half-way between Rebecca's and Natalie's heights. How tall is Stefanie?

cm
[1 mark]

2 At a school play, 326 tickets were sold.
Each ticket cost 55p.
How much money was raised altogether?

[1 mark]

3 Change these fractions into decimal numbers.

(a) $\frac{4}{5}$ (b) $\frac{2}{3}$ (c) $\frac{5}{8}$

[3 marks]

4 Calculate the length of each side of a square room, if the area of the room is 169 m².

m
[1 mark]

5 Write the missing number in this calculation.

$846.3 \div \boxed{} = 120.9$

[1 mark]

6 Use a calculator to work out the answer to this calculation.

$(39 + 16) \times (45 - 29) = \boxed{}$

[1 mark]   27

▶▶ **KEY** **POINTS**

> ▶ A percentage means the number of parts in every 100.
> ▶ A percentage can be worked out of any amount, not just 100.
> ▶ One whole = 100%   one half = 50%   one quarter = 25%
>   three quarters = 75%   one tenth = 10%

1 Part of the shape below is shaded.

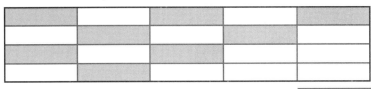

    (a) What percentage is shaded?   [%]

    (b) What percentage is **not** shaded?   [%]

[2 marks]

2 Calculate

    (a)   25% of 160 kg   [kg]

    (b)   60% of £50   [£   ]

[2 marks]

3 At a petrol station, the prices have been increased by 10%. Petrol used to cost 80p a litre.

    What is the new cost of a litre of petrol?   [P]

    How much will 10 litres cost at the new price?   [£   ]

[2 marks]

4 In a box of toy cars 9 are red.
This is 30% of the total number of cars in the box.

    (a) How many cars are in the box altogether?   [   ]

    (b) What percentage of the cars is not red?   [%]

[2 marks]

▶▶ KEY POINTS

▶ Fractions, decimals and percentages all show parts of something.

▶ $\frac{1}{2}$ = 50% = 0.5 $\frac{1}{4}$ = 25% = 0.25 $\frac{3}{4}$ = 75% = 0.75

$\frac{1}{10}$ = 10% = 0.1 $\frac{1}{100}$ = 1% = 0.01 $\frac{1}{5}$ = 20% = 0.2

▶ To change a percentage to a decimal, divide by 100.

▶ To change a decimal to a percentage, multiply by 100.

▶ To change a fraction to a decimal, divide the numerator by the denominator.

▶ A decimal fraction with one decimal place is written as tenths, eg, 0.9 = $\frac{9}{10}$

▶ A decimal fraction with two decimal places is written as hundredths, eg, 0.43 = $\frac{43}{100}$

▶ To change a percentage to a fraction, write the percentage over 100, eg, 73% = $\frac{73}{100}$

1 Complete the number sentences.

(a) 25% = 0.25 = [   ]   (b) 30% = [   ] = $\frac{3}{10}$ *[2 marks]*

2 Put a ring around the percentage which is equal to 0.35

3.5% $3\frac{1}{2}$ %   35%   350%   *[1 mark]*

3 Put a ring around the decimal fraction which is equal to $\frac{7}{100}$.

0.7   0.07   7.0   7.1   *[1 mark]*

4 Change 40% to a decimal and a fraction (in its simplest form).

Decimal ....   Fraction ....   *[2 marks]*

5 Use a calculator to write the following fractions as decimal fractions.

$\frac{1}{8}$ [   ] $\frac{3}{16}$ [   ]   *[2 marks]*

6 Put in the correct signs: <, > or = to complete these number sentences.

(a) 0.35 [   ] 35%   (b) $\frac{1}{4}$ [   ] 0.2   *[2 marks]*

29

▶▶ **KEY** POINTS

▶ A ratio compares one part with another.

▶ A proportion compares an amount to the whole.

▶ Ratios can be used in real-life situations, eg, to increase the amount of ingredients in a recipe.

▶ Proportions of amounts may be expressed as fractions of the whole.

1   Look at these shapes. Tick the statements that are correct.

The ratio of triangles to diamonds is 1 to every 3   ☐

The ratio of diamonds to triangles is 3 to every 2   ☐

The proportion of shapes that are diamonds is $\frac{3}{5}$ ☐

The proportion of shapes that are triangles is $\frac{4}{6}$ ☐   *[2 marks]*

2   Rachel has 30 sweets which she decides to share with Philip.
She gives Philip 2 sweets for every 3 she gives herself.
How many sweets will Philip receive?

[1 mark]

3 Here is a recipe for a cake that will serve eight people.

110g self-raising flour
110g sugar
110g margarine
2 eggs

How much sugar will be needed to make a cake
that will serve 12 people?

g

[I mark]

4 In a class of children, there are 6 right-handed children for every
one left-handed child.
There are 28 children in the class.
How many of them are left-handed?

[I mark]   31

▶▶ KEY POINTS

▶ The perimeter of a shape is the distance around the outside of the shape and is measured in mm, cm or m.

▶ The area of a shape is a measure of the amount of space covered by a plane shape and is measured in mm^2, cm^2 or m^2.

▶ The area of a rectangle may be found by multiplying together the length and breadth of the rectangle: area of a rectangle = l x b.

1 Put a tick inside the two shapes that have the same perimeter.

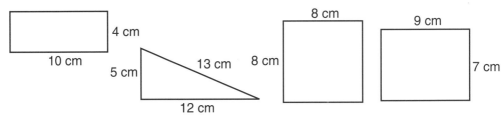

[1 mark]

2 The perimeter of this rectangle is 64 cm. The length of one of the long sides is 22 cm. What is the length of one of the short sides?

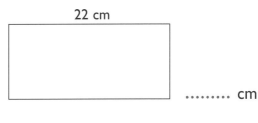

.... cm

[1 mark]

3 The shape on the grid below has an area of 6 cm^2. Draw two different shapes with an area of 6 cm^2.

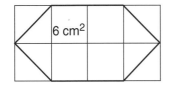

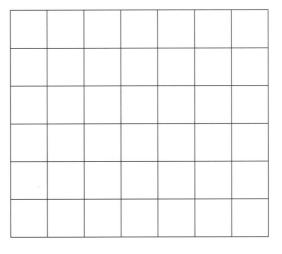

[2 marks]

4 Calculate both the perimeter and area of the shape.

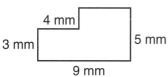

perimeter = [mm]

area = [mm²]   *[2 marks]*

5 (a) Measure the length and breadth of this rectangle.   *[1 mark]*

length = [cm]

breadth = [cm]

(b) Now use your answers to work out the area of the rectangle.

area = [cm²]   *[2 marks]*

6 Jane is making shapes using tiles.
These are the two tiles she uses.

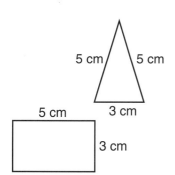

She makes this shape. What is the perimeter of the shape?

[cm]

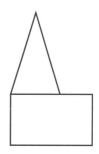

[1 mark]   **33**

▶▶ **KEY** POINTS

▶ The further a number on a number line is to the left, the smaller it is.
▶ The further a number on a number line is to the right, the larger it is.

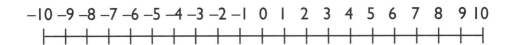

–10 –9 –8 –7 –6 –5 –4 –3 –2 –1   0   1   2   3   4   5   6   7   8   9 10

1 Write in the missing numbers to continue the sequence.

    8   5   2   –1   ☐   ☐   *[1 mark]*

2 What temperature does thermometer **A** show?

         ☐ °C

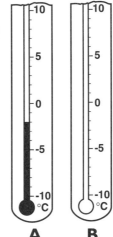

                                                 [1 mark]

The temperature drops by 5°C.
Mark the new temperature on thermometer **B**.

A   B

                                                     [1 mark]

3 This chart shows the temperatures every hour one morning in December.

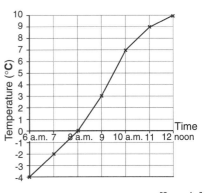

(a) What is the temperature at 6 a.m.?   ☐ °C

(b) What is the temperature rise between 7 a.m. and 10 a.m.?   ☐ °C

                                                     [2 marks]

▶▶ KEY POINTS

▶ To plot a point from its coordinates, first go across then up (or down).
▶ Perpendicular lines are at right angles to each other.
▶ Parallel lines are always the same distance apart.
▶ Two lines that cross each other are called intersecting lines.
▶ The eight compass directions are N, NE, E, SE, S, SW, W, NW.

1 Look at the map.

(a) Write down the
coordinates of
the church.

(b) Which feature has the
coordinates (43, 16)?

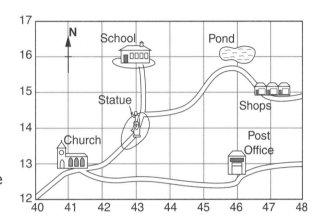

....

(c) Which feature is NW
of the Post Office? ....

[3 marks]

2 Plot the points on the grid using the coordinates below.

(3, 5)   (7, 5)   (7, 2)

[1 mark]

Plot another point
so that all four points
make a rectangle.
Join the points
to make a rectangle.

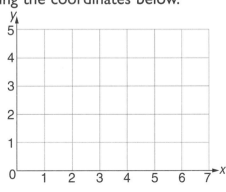

[1 mark]

3 Here is a graph.

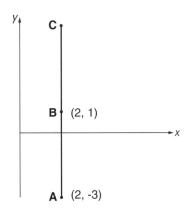

The points A, B and C are equally spaced.

(a) Write down the coordinates of the point C.   (,)

(b) Draw a line on the graph that is parallel to the line AC.

[2 marks]

4 Here is a graph.
There are two lines on the graph.

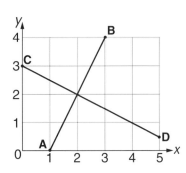

(a) Complete the sentence.

Line AB is .... to line CD.

(b) Write down the coordinates of the point
where the two lines intersect.   (,)

         [2 marks]

▶▶ KEY POINTS

▶ Reflection flips a shape over. The reflection is the same distance as the shape from the mirror line.
▶ A rotation turns the shape through an angle.
▶ Translation is a sliding movement – left/right or up/down.

1 Look at the triangles.

Complete the sentences.

(a) Triangle B is a .... of triangle A.

(b) Triangle .... is a reflection of triangle A.   *[2 marks]*

2 Draw the reflection of the shape in the mirror line.

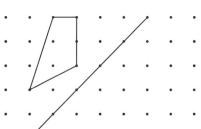

[1 mark]

3 The shape on the grid is to be translated four squares to the left. Draw its new position.
Write down the new coordinates of the point marked P.

New position of P = 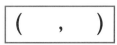 (,   )

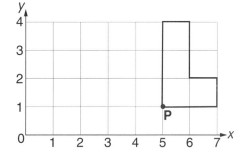

[1 mark]   **37**

▶▶ KEY POINTS

▶ 1 millennium = 1000 years; 1 century = 100 years; 1 decade = 10 years;
   1 year = 12 months or 52 weeks or 365 days (366 in a leap year);
   1 week = 7 days; 1 day = 24 hours; 1 hour = 60 minutes;
   1 minute = 60 seconds.

▶ To change a time from minutes to seconds, or from hours to minutes,
   multiply by 60.

▶ To change a time from seconds to minutes, or from minutes to hours,
   divide by 60.

1 The sign below shows the opening times for the local shop.

(a) How long is the shop open for
     on a Tuesday afternoon?

	Morning	Afternoon
Monday – Friday	7:00 – 12:00	13:00 – 17:30
Saturday	7:00 – 12:00	13:30 – 16:30
Sunday	10:00 – 12:00	closed

     [   ] hours

(b) Michael arrives at the shop on Sunday morning at 9:35.
     How much longer does he have to wait for the shop to open?

     [   ] minutes   *[2 marks]*

2 A video tape plays for 240 minutes. How long is this in hours?

     [   ] hours   *[1 mark]*

3 Two pages of a calendar are shown below.

	January					
Su	M	Tu	W	Th	F	Sa
1	2	3	4	5	6	7
8	9	10	11	12	13	14
15	16	17	18	19	20	21
22	23	24	25	26	27	28
29	30	31				

	February					
Su	M	Tu	W	Th	F	Sa
			1	2	3	4
5	6	7	8	9	10	11
12	13	14	15	16	17	18
19	20	21	22	23	24	25
26	27	28				

(a) On which day of the week
     does the 14th February fall?

     ....

(b) Write down the date that is 3 weeks after the 20th January.

....   *[2 marks)*

KEY POINTS

▶ Some problems can be solved in one step. Other problems may take two or more steps to solve.

▶ Work out how many steps are needed, identify the numbers to be used then read the words carefully and decide whether to use +, −, x or ÷ for each step.

1 Moin writes down a number.
He multiplies it by 15. His answer is 105.
What number did Moin write down?

[1 mark]

2 Deena makes bracelets using glass beads.
She uses 20 beads to make one bracelet.
Deena buys 450 beads.
How many bracelets can she make?

[1 mark]

3 Erin is doing a sponsored swim.
She needs 60 sponsors to fill her sponsor sheet.
Erin already has 38 names on her sheet.
13 friends have also agreed to sponsor her.
How many more sponsors does she need to find?

[1 mark]

4 Thomas wants to send Christmas cards to 50 friends.
He buys 2 packs of 12 cards, and 3 packs of 8 cards.
Does Thomas have enough cards to send to all of his friends?
Show your method.

....

....

[2 marks]   39

▶▶ KEY POINTS

▶ Identify the quantities to be used. Change the units of a quantity if necessary.

▶ Read the words carefully and decide whether to use +, –, x or ÷.

▶ Remember to give your answer in the correct units.

1 The Post Office sells stamps like those shown below:

(a) It costs Bryony 24p to send a letter.
Which two stamps does she buy?

☐ p ☐ p

(b) It costs Bryony 90p to send a parcel.
Which three stamps does she buy?

☐ p ☐ p ☐ p

[2 marks]

2 For every £5 Jake makes washing cars, his mother gives him an extra £2.
After 6 weeks Jake has made £30 washing cars.
How much money will his mother have to give him?

£ ☐

How much does he have altogether?

£ ☐

[2 marks]

3 Krispy Pops breakfast cereal is normally sold in packets of 380 g.
As a special offer, packets now contain 50% extra free.

How much cereal is in the special offer packet?

☐ g

[1 mark]

4 Joshua's father wants to put a decorative paper border around the living room.
The perimeter of the room is 17 m.
Each roll of paper border is 4.5 m long.

How many rolls does Joshua's father need to buy?

☐ rolls

[1 mark]

1 Write in the missing numbers.

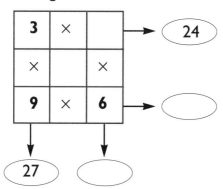

[2 marks)

2 Write in the missing digits.

 5 + 9 ⬚ = 1 7 1   [1 mark]

3 Here is a multiplication fact.

54 × 79 = 4266

Explain how you could use this fact to work out the answer to this calculation.

54 x 7.9 =

....

.... [1 mark]

4 Write the same number in each box to make the calculation correct.

You may use a calculator.

⬚ x ⬚ = 256   [1 mark]

1 (a) What is the name of this shape?

....

(b) Explain how you know.

....

....

[2 marks]

2 Add two extra squares to the shape in the diagram so that it has one line of symmetry.

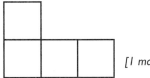

[1 mark]

3 Hannah and Alex have both been asked to draw a shape which has a **perimeter of 8 cm** and an **area of 4 cm²**.
Their shapes are shown below on a centimetre-squared grid.

Hannah 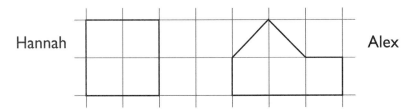 Alex

Which shape does not fit the description?
Circle either Hannah or Alex.   HANNAH   ALEX

Explain your answer.

.... *[1 mark]*

▶▶ KEY POINTS

▶ A general statement can be tested by finding examples that match it.
▶ Symbols can be used to give rules, eg, $l \times b$, $3n$, $m + n$.

1 Oliver says:

> **"If you multiply a three-digit number by a single-digit number you will never get a five-digit number."**

Use a calculator to investigate whether Oliver is correct.

Circle yes or no.   YES   NO

Explain your answer.

....

.... *[1 mark]*

2 Steve says that the sum of three consecutive numbers is always a multiple of three. Find examples to show whether this is true.

....

.... *[2 marks]*

3 Imran knows that a number is divisible by four if its last two digits are divisible by four.

He knows that he can use this rule to work out which years are leap years.

Use this rule to find the dates of four leap years.

[2 marks] **43**

4 Write the following rules using symbols.
Use the letter **n** to stand for a number.

One has been done for you.

(a) the difference between a number and 6   **n – 6**

(b) a number added to 10   ....

(c) 7 multiplied by a number   ....

(d) double a number and add 1   ....

[3 marks]

5 Complete the table.

m	m + 4
5	9
11	
	18

[2 marks]

6 The formula for the sequence   **3, 6, 9, 12, ...** is **3n**

The formula for the sequence   **4, 7, 10, 13, ...** is **3n + 1**

What is the formula for the sequence **2, 5, 8, 11, ...** ?

[1 mark]